Tweenies™

Annual 2003

This fun-a-rooney annual
belongs to

_____

Hey, hey, are you ready to play?
It's time to come and play with the Tweenies.
Hey, hey, what do you say?
Come along and play with the Tweenies.

First published in 2002 by BBC Worldwide Limited
Woodlands, 80 Wood Lane
London W12 0TT
Written and adapted by Sara Carroll
Make Its devised by Natalie Abadzis
Illustrations by Alan Craddock, Andy Holt, Leo Hartas,
Stephanie Longfoot and Bill Titcombe
Photography by John Englefield
With thanks to Tyana, Loretta, Olivia and Rachid
Text, design and illustrations © 2002 BBC Worldwide Limited
Tweenies © 1998 BBC
Tweenies © 1999 BBC Worldwide Limited
Tweenies is produced by Tell-Tale Productions Ltd for the BBC.
ISBN 0 563 53237 8
Printed and bound in Belgium

Tweenie clock – where will it stop?

Come on everybody! Let's sing

The Farmer's in His Den

The farmer's in his den.

The farmer's in his den.

E-I-E-I The farmer's in his den.

The farmer wants a wife.

The farmer wants a wife.

E-I-E-I The farmer wants a wife.

The wife wants a child.
The wife wants a child.
E-I-E-I The wife wants a child.

The child wants a nurse.
The child wants a nurse.
E-I-E-I The child wants a nurse.

The nurse wants a dog.
The nurse wants a dog.
E-I-E-I The nurse wants a dog.

We all pat the dog.
We all pat the dog.
E-I-E-I We all pat the dog.

7

Fizz's Farmyard Scrapbook

I went to stay on a farm. I helped the farmer and I learnt how to look after the animals. I took some photos and then I made this scrapbook to tell the story of my visit.

Cow

There were lots of cows but my favourite was called Tinkerbell. The farmer's wife makes delicious yoghurt and ice cream from her milk.

Pig

I liked the pigs best. They make a snuffly sound and their curly tails are so sweet. Pigs are very messy eaters!

Sheep

One day we went to see the sheep in their field. This one kept following Fizz. I fed her grass by holding it flat in my hand. It tickled!

Hen

The hens did lots of clucking and scratching. They can lay their eggs anywhere. We even found one on the seat of the tractor!

Dog

Ruffle, the sheep dog, helps the farmer round up the sheep. He is very friendly but he loves to chase the ducks when he's not working.

Tractor, trailer, farmer

Here is Farmer Headcorn on his tractor. I had a ride in the trailer one day. It was a bit bumpy!

Here I am on my last day. I had a lovely time on the farm. Next time I come I want to bring my friends so they can see the animals, too.

9

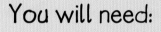
messy time

Cotton-reel Cows
(and pigs and sheep)

Make a collection of cotton-reel farm animals with a stable for them to live in.

You will need:

Cotton reels

Coloured card

A black pen

Safe scissors

Glue

A large sheet of coloured paper

A large cardboard tub with a lid

A grown-up to help

To make the animals:

1 To make a pig, place a cotton reel on its end on a piece of pink card to measure for size.

2 Use the black pen to draw the two ends of the animal – a front view and a back view.

10

3 Cut out the two ends of the pig.

4 Glue the front view onto one end of the cotton reel and the back view onto the other.

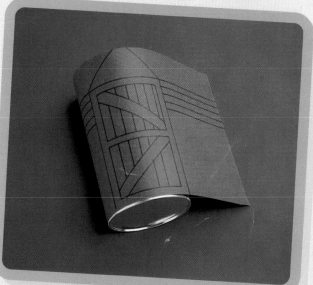

You can use this same method to make a cotton-reel cow, sheep or chick.

To make the stable:

1 Draw a stable onto some coloured paper.

2 Glue the paper onto the tub.

Now your farm is ready to play with.

Milo's Animal Jokes

I love animal jokes. Don't you?
Here are some of my favourites.

Knock knock.
Who's there?
Cows go.
Cows go who?
No, silly, cows go moo!

Moo Moo Moo

Bah Bah Bah

What do you get if you cross a sheep with six radiators?
Central bleating.

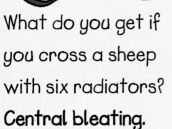

What's a frog's favourite flower?
A croakus.

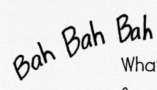

Where do frogs keep their money.
In the river bank.

How do you catch a squirrel?
Climb up a tree and act like a nut.

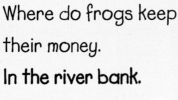

What do birds eat between meals?
Tweets!

Tweet Tweet

What do bees say when they fly backwards?
Zub! Zub!

12

Puzzle Fun on the Farm

Which two animals don't live on a farm?

Answer: the parrot and the giraffe

Can you help Milo push the tractor to Bella through the sandpit maze?

A Bit of Fairy Magic

Bella, Milo, Fizz, Jake and Doodles have dressed up as some of their favourite fairy-tale characters, and Judy has made up a story about them.
Match the little pictures in the story to the key to find the missing words.

One day in Make-believe Land, four fairy-tale people were feeling sad.  needed someone to chase the  who kept following her, the  was looking for a beautiful princess to marry, the  was bored with no s to chase and one of the s simply wanted someone to marry her.

"It's all very well, living in Make-believe Land," said , "but we all need a bit of magic to help things along from time to time."

At that moment there was a puff of magic dust and a  appeared.

"You lot look down in the dumps," she tinkled. "I wonder if I can help." So 🧺, the 👑, the ⚔️ and the 🐺 all told her why they were so miserable. The 🧚 laughed. "Oh you sillies! The answers to your problems are right in front of your noses! All you need is a little 🧚 magic."

She did a pirouette, waved her ✨ and in one second less than no time the ⚔️ was chasing the 🐺 away from 🧺, while the 👑 took a closer look at the 🐺, thought she was the most beautiful princess he had ever seen and asked her to marry him.

The 🧚 put away her ✨ and looked around. "Well, that was a job well done! I do like it when everyone lives happily ever after!"

Key

Little Red Riding Hood   Wicked Wolf   Prince   Knight   Dragon   Ugly Sister   Fairy   Wand

Colour By Numbers

Can you colour in this scene from the story, 'A Bit of Fairy Magic', using the numbers and the colour chart to guide you?

messy time

16

17

Looking After Doodles

"Why can't Doodles get his own food?" asked
Fizz one day, when Judy was feeding Doodles.

"Because he can't put food into his own bowl," said Judy. "Dogs like
Doodles need looking after."

"Is looking after Doodles the same as looking after children?" asked Milo.
Judy shook her head. "No, it isn't," she said.

"Can we try to look after Doodles?" begged Bella. "**Please?**"

"All right," Judy agreed. "I'll be close by if you need any help."

Fizz had the first turn. She put ribbons
in Doodles' hair to make him look pretty.
Then she put a nappy on him.

"Dogs don't wear nappies!" barked
Doodles. He didn't like the nappy at all.

"There's nothing to be ashamed of,"
Fizz insisted. "We've all had to wear them."

When it was Milo's turn, he fastened a bib around Doodles' neck.

"Dogs don't wear bibs!" woofed Doodles.

"You have to keep your fur nice and clean," said Milo. "Now, open wide – dinner time!" and he tried to pop a sandwich into Doodles' mouth. But Doodles didn't want a sandwich.

When it was Bella's turn, she said she'd take him for a walk. Doodles raced to the door, barking loudly and wagging his tail.

"WAIT!" ordered Bella. "First you have to get dressed."

"It's a nice sunny day," said Bella. "This shirt will be cool. Sunglasses will keep the sun out of your eyes. And a hat will stop your head from burning."

At last Doodles was ready for his walk.

"But dogs don't wear clothes!" he whined.

19

Milo followed Bella and Doodles into the garden.
"Doodles won't eat his sandwich," he complained.
"Dogs don't eat sandwiches," said Bella. "They eat
meat and bones."
"Where does Doodles keep his bones?" asked Milo.
"Dogs bury their bones," said Bella. "Where do you
bury bones, Doodles?"

"I buried one in a very safe
place," Doodles barked, "but
I can't remember where."
So he started digging, and
he dug and he dug until he
found his bone.

"Clever boy, Doodles!"
said Bella.

Just then he heard
someone calling him,
"Doodles, Doodles!" It
was Jake and he
scampered indoors.

20

Jake laughed when he saw Doodles.
"You look funny!" he teased.
Doodles barked and
chased Jake, and they
rolled together all over
the floor.

Off came
    the hat,
        the sunglasses,
            the ribbons,
                the clothes,
                    the nappy...

"STOP THAT!" yelled Fizz.

Bella and Fizz went to find Judy.

"Jake's messed up Doodles," they told her.

"I didn't mean to," cried Jake. "I was
only playing with him. Anyway,
Doodles looked silly in clothes!"
"No, he didn't!" said Bella. "He looked
beautiful. And he was cool and dry
and clean and everything."

"Jake's right," said Judy. "Dogs don't need to wear clothes. Doodles isn't like you or me. Doodles is a dog. He needs to be looked after just like a dog."

"What special things does Doodles need?" asked Fizz.

"Dogs need long walks, big bones, water, dog food and lots of love," said Judy.

"And dogs like to play," added Jake.

"Woof!" barked Doodles. "That's what I like BEST!"

22

The End

Meet Izzles

There is a newcomer to the Tweenie playroom. She's pretty, cuddly, bouncy and fun. She likes long, muddy walks and playing hide and seek.

Her favourite food is crunchy dog biscuits and her favourite toy is her very noisy, squeaky bone. She's only a puppy and everyone loves her, especially Doodles! Welcome Izzles!

Izzles' Game

Izzles is getting to know everyone, and the Tweenies have made up some puzzles to help her learn more about them.

Can you help Izzles return Bella, Fizz, Milo, Jake and Doodles' favourite things to them by following the coloured ribbons?

Izzles, Izzles! Mine is blue and white.

Izzles! Mine's pink.

Answer: 5

Answer: 4

24

Can you help Izzles solve the Tweenies' colour clues and find their bean bags?

The Tweenies are showing Izzles how old they are. Can you count the fingers and thumbs and write the ages in the boxes next to each Tweenie?

Colouring-in

The Tweenies have made up a special song to welcome Izzles. It's called 'Hi there, Izzles!' Sing along with the Tweenies and Doodles as you colour in the picture.

Hi there, Izzles!
It's great to have you here!
Tip top Izzles!
Just listen to us cheer.
Your fur is purple,
Your eyes are bright.
You're very very bouncy,
But we think that you're all right!

Hi there, Izzles!
We hope you're going to stay.
Good girl, Izzles!
There's so much to do each day.
You can play with Doodles
And share in all our fun.
So come and meet the Tweenie gang.
Shout WOOF WOOF everyone!

27

An Izzles Secret Storage Box

Make your own Izzles secret storage box. When the lid is shut, only you will know what is inside!

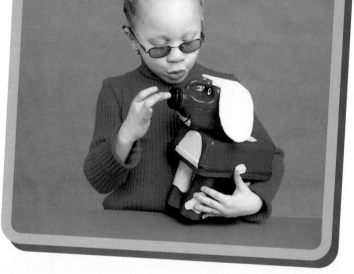

You will need:

A one kilo ice cream box

Four toilet rolls

Sticky tape

One small plastic milk container

Glue

Purple, pale yellow, black and white poster paint

A black pen

A paint brush

A thin, yellow kitchen sponge

Safe scissors

A grown-up to help

1 Tape the four toilet rolls onto the lid of the ice cream box.

2 Glue on the milk container on the base for the head.

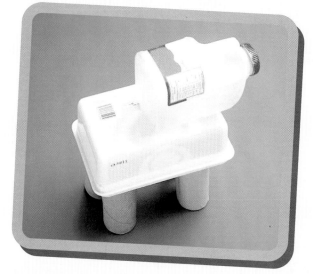

3 Paint Izzles with white paint to cover up the packaging. When it is dry, paint Izzles with purple and pale yellow poster paint and leave to dry. Then paint on eyes and a nose.

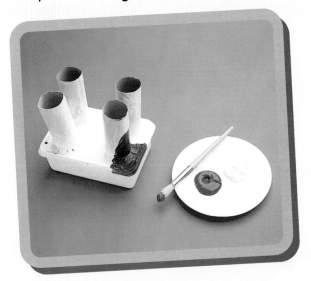

4 Draw ears and a tail on the yellow kitchen sponge.

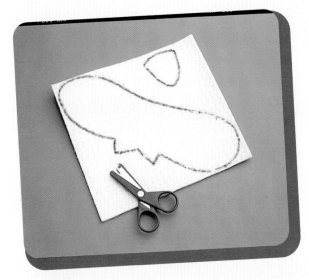

5 Cut them out and glue them onto Izzles. Paint the tail purple.

Now you are ready to store whatever you want in your secret storage box.

29

It's a Teeny Tiny World

surprise time

One morning, Judy brought in a dolls house for the Tweenies to look at. She told them how it used to be hers when she was little.

"Does that mean Judy was little enough to go inside," laughed Milo.

"No, Milo! It was Judy's when she was *your* age," said Fizz.

Bella stared at the tiny front door and sighed.

"Imagine if *you* were tiny enough to walk round a dolls house," she said. "I would live in it and invite all my teeny tiny Tweenie friends for tea!"

"If I were teeny tiny," said Fizz, "I would climb into the cage with Tiny, my pet mouse, and keep him company."

"If I were teeny tiny," said Milo, "I'd *jump* on to the back of a passing bird and fly as high as the sky."

"If I were teeny tiny." said Jake, "I would climb up Max's back and sit in his waistcoat pocket so I wouldn't have to walk anywhere, and I'd have a wonderful view."

 "If we were teeny tiny," barked Doodles and Izzles, "our bones would take much longer to eat. Yum, yum!"

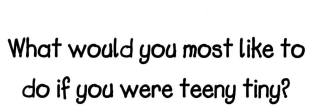

What would you most like to do if you were teeny tiny?

Frog's New Home

Here's a chance to make your very own teeny tiny Tweenie book. Cut out the page opposite, follow the step-by-step instructions, and you will have a book to slip into your pocket and read whenever you want.

1 Cut along the dotted lines ....

2 Fold the little pages along the folding lines _ _ _ _ _ _

3 Put them together in the right page order to make the book.

4 Put an elastic band around the pages to keep them together.

"Love it, love it!"

croaked Norman.

The End

2

Tweenies™
Frog's New Home

1

"Off you go!" said Max, and
Norman took a big hop.

0

Jake and Fizz went
outside to see what
Doodles had found.

"It's a dragon!"
shrieked Jake.

3

...where there was
a huge pond.

"No, Jake!" laughed Fizz.
"Frogs don't live in HOUSES!
They live in water!"

"Well, Jake, I
think we should
take Norman
home," said Max.

3

5

One day, Doodles found something SCARY in the garden.

2

"Do you like your new home, Norman?" asked Jake.

1

"That's not a dragon – it's a frog!" said Fizz.

"Dear me," said Max. "It's a long way from home."

"He's not an 'it'. He's Norman and he's my best friend!" said Jake, scooping up the frog. "Can he live in our playhouse?"

4

"I think you will be happier here than in our garden," Jake whispered.

"Come on, Norman," said Max. "We're going on a trip to find you some water."

Max put Norman in a plastic box with holes in the lid...

...and Jake carried him all the way to the park...

6

The Game of Beetle

You will need a dice and some paper and pencils.

This is a little creepy crawly game for two or more players. Take it in turns to throw the dice and draw a beetle like this – when you get a 6 draw a body, then you need a 1 for a head. You can add the other bits in any order when you get the right numbers on the dice – just follow the diagram.

The first person to complete their drawing shouts, **"Beetle!"** and is the winner.

6 – body
1 – head
3 – eyes
4 – antennae
2 – legs

Creepy Crawly Minibeasts

The Tweenies have been learning about minibeasts with Max and Judy. Can you spot which creature they are each talking about?

This minibeast has eight legs.

Answer: spider

This one is red and has black spots.

Answer: ladybird

My minibeast carries her home on her back.

Answer: snail

Puzzle Time

Can you find ten little yellow birds in the park?

Colour by letters!

Use the code to colour the picture and find out what it is.

Colour Code

p =
r =
y =
o =
g =

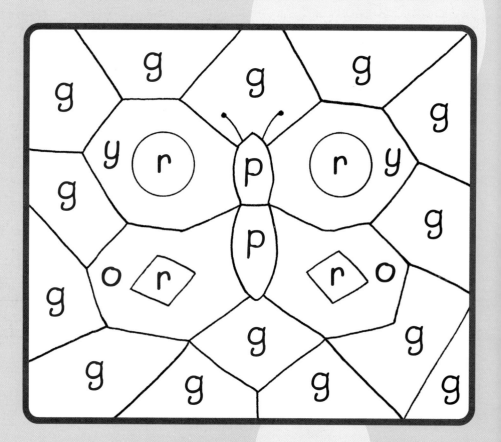

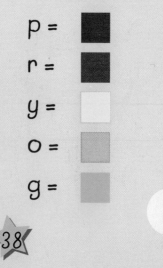

Can you spot five differences between the two pictures?

Answer: The magician's coat is green, there is an extra candle, one of the parcels is missing, one of the balloons is missing and the teddy bear's hat is striped.

Dream Show

The Tweenies were watching some pop stars on the television.

It was rather loud and Judy asked them to turn it down a little, but that didn't make much difference because Bella and Fizz carried on singing loudly and Milo couldn't keep his feet still.

"I'd love to be a glamorous pop star and sing in a band," said Fizz.

"And wear all those sparkly clothes," said Jake.

"And I'd like to boogie and groove to the music, man!" said Milo.

"I know!" Bella jumped up. "Let's make our own pop group and do a dream show."

"But we need all the glittery stuff!" said Jake.

"OK," said Bella. "Let's just pretend..."

Here we are in our glittery pop star clothes.

Doodles and Izzles want to
be pop stars, too!

Max sings a song about us.

Spotty monsters join
us on stage.

Milo boogies and grooves all
by himself. He loves it!

Lots of poeple are watching us, but we
don't feel nervous at all!

Dream Show Collage Fun

The Tweenies have made up a song for their dream show. Colour in the pictures and stick on glittery bits to make them look like real pop stars. Then sing along with the Tweenies!

I want to sing in a band
And make you clap your hands.

I want to dance to the beat
And make you move your feet.

I want to shimmy in the night
And be an awesome sight.

I want to be a pop star,
a pop star, yeah!

I want to be stylish,
Play the coolest sound.

I want the fans to love me
And follow me around.

With my crazy hair
I'll make people stare.

I want to be a pop star,
a pop star, yeah!
I want to be a pop star.

Oh yeah!

43

Pop Star Glasses

Glitter your way to pop-stardom with these Tweenies pop star glasses!

You will need:

Tracing paper

Red card

Safe scissors

Glue

Glitter

A grown-up to help

1. Trace the heart-shaped glasses template onto tracing paper.

2. Copy the glasses image from tracing paper onto red card.

3. Cut out the glasses shape. Ask the grown-up to help you.

4 Add glue to the glasses and sprinkle on some glitter.

5 Wait until the glue is dry. Now your glasses are ready to wear!

Template

Why don't you try making some Tweenies glasses in different shapes and colours.

45

Doctor, Baker, Cobbler, Sailor

The Tweenies have been learning rhymes about the jobs people do. Here are some of their favourites.

Miss Polly had a Dolly

Miss Polly had a dolly
Who was sick sick sick,
So she phoned for the doctor
To come quick quick quick.

The doctor came
With a bag and a hat,
And she knocked at the door
With a rat-a-tat-tat.

She looked at the dolly
And she shook her head,
And said, "Miss Polly,
Put her straight to bed."

Cobbler, Cobbler

Cobbler, cobbler, mend my shoe,
Get it done by half past two.
Half past two is much too late,
Get it done by half past eight.

A Sailor Went to Sea

A sailor went to sea sea sea,
To see what he could see see see.
But all that he could see see see,
Was the bottom of the
deep blue sea sea sea.

Pat-a-Cake

Pat-a cake, pat-a cake
Baker's man.
Bake me a cake,
As fast as you can.
Pat it and prick it
And mark it with B
And put it in the oven for
Baby and me.

Now they have dressed up as the busy people in the rhymes. Can you match each rhyme to one of the Tweenies?

Busy People

The Tweenies are watching a video about jobs. Can you match the little pictures of busy people to the big picture? Which job would you like to do?

delivery man

computer programmer

postwoman

painter

cook

window cleaner

greengrocer

baker

Dream Biscuits

Jake and Milo are dreaming about what they would like to be when they grow up. Jake wants to be a train driver and Milo wants to be a spaceman. To help them make their dreams come true, here is a recipe for making Dream Biscuits.

You will need:

Biscuit dough

A pencil

Greaseproof paper

Safe scissors

Icing sugar

Smarties

A grown-up to help

Biscuit Dough recipe

100g soft butter
175g caster sugar
One egg
A teaspoon of
vanilla essence
225g sifted plain flour

Cream the butter with the caster sugar, and then beat in the egg and the vanilla essence. Gradually add the plain flour and combine into a soft dough. Put the dough in the fridge for a couple of hours.

Template

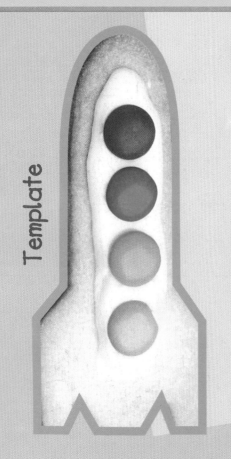

1. Trace the rocket and train templates onto the greaseproof paper. Cut them out.

2. Roll out the biscuit dough on a floured surface.

3. Place the templates on the dough.

4. Ask a grown-up to cut rocket and train shapes out of the dough.

5. Ask a grown-up to place the biscuits on a greased baking tray and cook in the oven for about 10 minutes on 350° Fahrenheit/gas mark 6 or until golden brown.

6. Leave the biscuits to cool down. You are now ready to decorate them with Smarties, and icing sugar and water mixed together.

Template

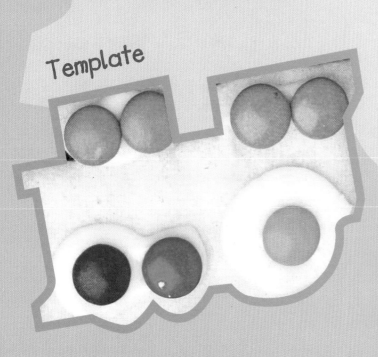

Time to get munching –
and dreaming!

Guess What I Do! Card Game

You will need safe scissors.

This is one of Max's favourite games that you can play with two or more friends. Ask a grown-up to help you cut out the picture cards on the page opposite. Then make a pile of the cards face down on the floor.

The first player picks up the top card and looks at it secretly. Then he or she must act out the job shown on the card to the others, without using any words. The rest of the players have to guess the job.

If they guess correctly, that player keeps the card. If they can't work it out then the card goes at the bottom of the pile. Players take it in turns to pick up cards and act out the jobs.

The winner is the person with the most cards.

Dentist

Teacher

Astronaut

Singer

Footballer

Builder

Lorry driver

Cook

Hairdresser

Gardener

Ballet dancer

Photographer

Colour In and Dot-to-Dot

The Tweenies have drawn some dot-to-dot pictures. Can you join the dots and see what they are? Then colour the scene.

The Rabbit, the Frog, the Duck, the Swan and the Wolf

The Tweenies have decided to tell you a story. Are you ready to hear it?

It was a beautiful day in the grassy meadow. **"Te-te-te-te-te,"** chattered the rabbit as she grazed among the daisies.

Just then a frog came jumping by. **"Ribbit, ribbit,"** croaked the frog. "Where are you going?" asked the rabbit.

"Down to the river to see the swan dance."

"Oh, wait for me and I'll come with you," said the rabbit.

So the rabbit **te-te-te-te-te** followed the frog **ribbit ribbit** across the grassy meadow.

Just then a duck came waddling by.
"**Quack quack,**" said the duck when he saw the rabbit and the frog. "Where are you going?"
"Down to the river to see the swan dance."
"Oh, wait for me and I will come with you," said the duck.

So the duck **quack quack** followed the rabbit **te-te-te-te-te** and the rabbit **te-te-te-te-te** followed the frog **ribbit ribbit** down to the river to see the swan dance.

And there they saw a beautiful swan gliding **swish swish** across the water.

But suddenly...

...SNARL SNARL a big bad wolf arrived!
The frog **ribbit ribbit** and the duck **quack quack**
jumped **splish splash** into the river, but the rabbit
te-te-te-te-te could not swim.

So the rabbit **te-te-te-te-te** stood nose to nose with
the big bad wolf SNARL SNARL.

Then...

"GO AWAY, BIG BAD WOLF AND LEAVE US ALONE,"

yelled the brave rabbit.

The big bad wolf was so surprised...

...he ran off as fast as he could.

"**YIPPEE!**" cheered the rabbit, the frog, the duck and the swan – but not the wolf!

The End

news time

We Hope You've Had a Lovely Time

We hope you've had a lovely time reading this Tweenies annual. Can you remember which were your favourite pages? Perhaps you liked meeting 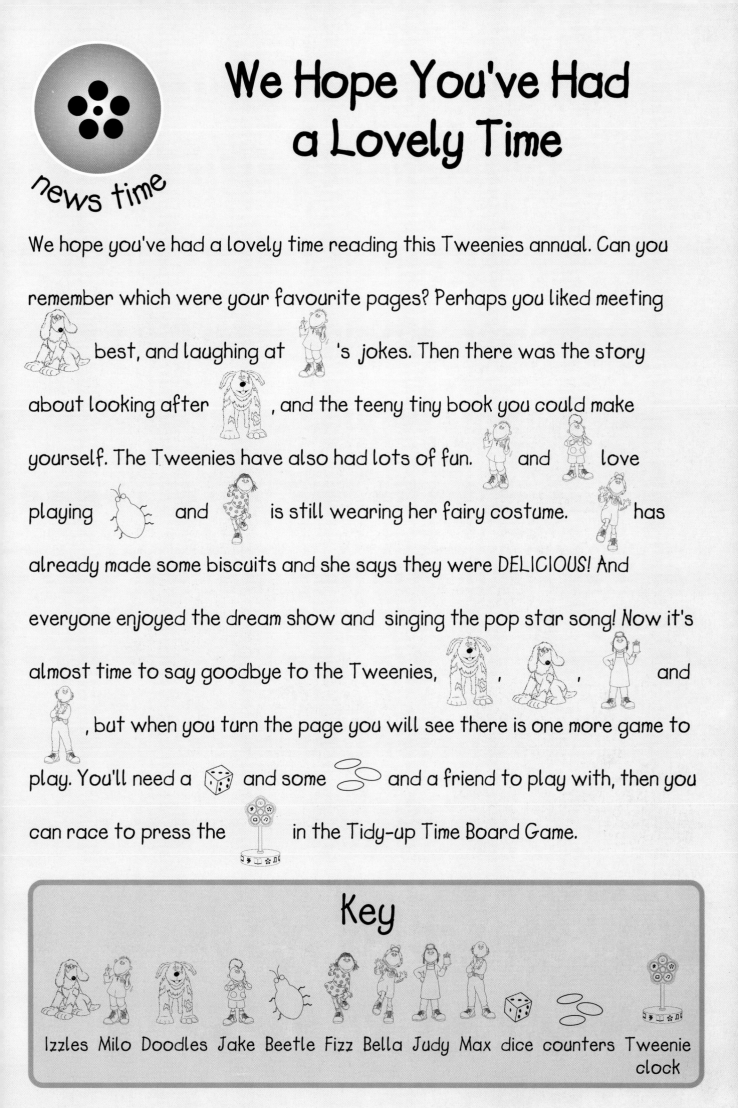 best, and laughing at 's jokes. Then there was the story about looking after , and the teeny tiny book you could make yourself. The Tweenies have also had lots of fun. and love playing and is still wearing her fairy costume. has already made some biscuits and she says they were DELICIOUS! And everyone enjoyed the dream show and singing the pop star song! Now it's almost time to say goodbye to the Tweenies, , , and , but when you turn the page you will see there is one more game to play. You'll need a and some and a friend to play with, then you can race to press the in the Tidy-up Time Board Game.

Key

Izzles Milo Doodles Jake Beetle Fizz Bella Judy Max dice counters Tweenie clock

Tidy-up Time Board Game

It's tidy-up time and the end of the day – see if you can help the Tweenies and have some fun at the same time. When you land on a green square you have to sing one of the Tweenies' favourite songs before jumping ahead four spaces. The winner gets to press the Tweenie clock at the end.

You will need a dice and some counters.

Start

♫ song time

Spill red paint in the messy corner. Miss a go while you clear it up.

Stop to play with Milo and his racing car. Miss a go.

♫ song time

Help Doodles look for his bone. Go forward 1.

Help Fizz tidy the teddies. Go forward 2.

♫ song time